WRITE ABOUT YOUR DREAMS

Good things ahead

BE YOU X 2

SHARE YOUR DREAM

SHARE the JOURNEY

D1623070

SAVOR

COLLABORATOR

COMMUNICATOR

BE LIKE THE ROCK IN THE MIDDLE OF THE RIVER AND LET THE WATER FLOW AROUND YOU.

dream deeply

BU times 2

Navigate creatively

Be free to be you

Dream

BUMPS IN THE ROAD ARE JUST PART OF THE JOURNEY

Believe

FIND YOUR ELEMENT

JOURNEY WITH JOY

BE JUST A BIT BRAVER THAN YOU WERE PLANNING TO BE

POWER THROUGH

BREATHE

HAPPY
DREAMER

by PETER H. REYNOLDS

ORCHARD BOOKS

AN IMPRINT of SCHOLASTIC INC.
NEW YORK

I AM A HAPPY DREAMER.

I'm really good at dreaming.

DAY DREAMS.

BIG DREAMS.

Little dreams.

CREATIVE DREAMS.

dreamer maximus!

But my dreams have a mind of their own.

SOMETIMES MY MIND JUST TAKES FLIGHT! I HEAR A **BEAT** AND I GOTTA MOVE...

THEN I HEAR ANOTHER AND ANOTHER!

TRUMPETY, ZIGZAG JAZZ!

when I make time
to stay still and
hear myself think—
to let go and see
what takes shape.

DO YOU SEE THAT?

Sometimes I'm a swing-high dreamer... WAY UP HIGH...BEYOND THE CLOUDS...

SO HIGH I CAN TOUCH THE SKY!

I can also be a **LOUD** dreamer!

HELLO,

WORLD!

I'M A SHOUT-AT-THE-TOP-OF-MY-LUNGS DREAMER!
(EVEN IF I'M JUST A LOUD-INSIDE-MY-HEAD DREAMER!)

SOMETIMES...

I'M A COLORFUL DREAMER,

PAINTING MY OWN PATH
FULL OF SURPRISES AT EVERY TURN.

I can dream
even when the
lights are **OUT**.

ALL CIRCUITS ON!
FIREWORKS!
I LIGHT UP!
I'M ALL EARS,
EYES, HEART, AND MIND!

I have so many dreams it can get messy.
CREATIVE CHAOS.

Cleaning up hides my treasures.

If YOU MAKE ME,
I will put my things away.
But then there is
less ME to show.

These are the moments
I feel alone.

BOXED IN.

And yet, I always find a way back.

Plunging into amazing, delightful, happy dreams.

I'm really good at being me.

A DREAMER

SURPRISING

CARING

FUNNY

GENTLE

SMART

And when I
TUMBLE
back to earth...

I know I'm okay!

Dreamers have a way of bouncing back...

AND MOVING FORWARD!

WINGED DREAMER

ROYAL DREAMER

THINKING DREAMER

SWEET DREAMER

SUNNY DREAMER

FLOATING DREAMER

LOVE DREAMER

WILD DREAMER

CRAZY DREAMER

POWER DREAMER

CIVIC DREAMER

VOTE for ME

SECRET DREAMER

ICE CREAM HAPPY

SUNSHINE HAPPY

MAKE A DIFFERENCE HAPPY

NAP HAPPY

MUSIC HAPPY

DANCE HAPPY

PEACEFUL HAPPY

CATCH HAPPY

KINDNESS HAPPY

AWE HAPPY

SILLY HAPPY

FOOT-STOMPIN' HAPPY

THERE ARE SO MANY WAYS TO BE A

HAPPY DREAMER!

(WHAT KIND OF DREAMER ARE YOU?)

DREAMY DREAMER

TEAM DREAMER

VISION DREAMER

GOAL DREAMER

STAGE DREAMER

STELLAR DREAMER

NIGHT DREAMER

DAYDREAMER

BIG DREAMER

SPACE DREAMER

FIERCE DREAMER

GIANT DREAMER

DIZZY HAPPY

ART HAPPY

MOVE HAPPY

HARD WORK HAPPY

CELEBRATION HAPPY

LAUGH HAPPY

NATURE HAPPY

DISCOVERY HAPPY

FAMILY HAPPY

ALONE HAPPY

FRIENDS HAPPY

OCEAN HAPPY

But the **best** way
to be a happy dreamer?

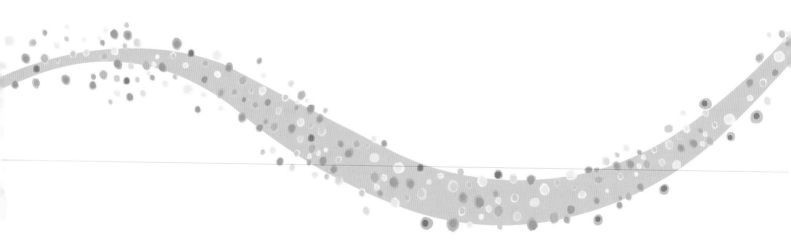

Just BE YOU.

Which is why this book is dedicated to you. YES, YOU!